Sanjeev Kapoor's

Tasty Eating
for Healthy Living

In association with Alyona Kapoor

- Volume Two -

PopulaR
prakashan

www.popularprakashan.com

Published by:

POPULAR PRAKASHAN PVT. LTD.

301, Mahalaxmi Chambers

22, Bhulabhai Desai Road

Mumbai 400 026

for **KHANA KHAZANA PUBLICATIONS PVT. LTD.**

(4305)

ISBN – 978-81-7991-557-8

Nutritionist: Kirti Masurkar

Book Design: Pratibha Gurnani Creative

Photography: Bharat Bhirangi, Alim Bolar

Food Stylist: Anupa Das

Printed in India

Standard Press (India) Pvt. Ltd.,

34G, Poothayammal Nagar,

Near YRTV School, Sivakasi - 626 123.

contents

i am fit!

Fitness has different definitions for different people.
A teenager will say 'I am fit' because he or she has great stamina or enthusiasm.
A housewife might say 'I am fit' as she does not feel tired after all the housework is done.
Grandma might say 'I am fit' as she does not have aches and pains.
A runner might say 'I am fit' as he or she clocked the best time ever in the last race!
As a definition, fitness means to live healthily - mentally and physically.

control stress

If one wants to maintain mental as well as physical health then the first requirement is to control stress. Basically it is the reaction of the body to any change requiring some sort of adjustment that can be either physical or mental. Hence controlling it is essential if one wants to be mentally and physically fit.

Stress is both good and bad. Some stress causes alertness and motivates one to achieve the desired goals. Excess stress is bad and it can lead to mental sickness or depression. Leading a healthy lifestyle can help reduce the stress level in life and make one more resilient and help cope with the major stressors in life. Adapting to a healthy lifestyle means that one can concentrate better, have more energy and have increased stamina. Starting with the proper diet and nutrition plan is the best foundation for a healthy life.

stress busters

❶ Carbohydrates, proteins, fats, vitamins and minerals are all important for energy, mental concentration and emotional stability, as long as they are eaten with moderation. Anyone is likely to become sick when the body is stressed as the immune system is not working at its full capacity. A healthy, well-balanced diet keeps one healthy even in times of stress.

❷ Stress makes one reach out for foods loaded with sugar and grease. During stressful times it is noticed that the choice of foods high in fat, sodium and calories always aggravates the situation. One can try taking vitamin pills or supplements, but there is no alternative to a balanced healthy meal.

❸ Start the day with a healthy breakfast, followed by a light balanced lunch, a fruit as a snack and then a simple non-spicy dinner that is not too late in the night. This plan lays the best foundation for defense against stress. Be alert and have more fruit, vegetables, whole grains, fat-free/low-fat milk and milk products, lean meat, poultry, fish, beans, eggs and nuts.

boost the memory

Food can help to enhance the memory. These memory enhancers are recommended carbohydrates that are high in fibre and low in sugar. High-fibre foods stay in our system for longer periods and do not give the quick rise in blood sugar that one can get from foods made from refined flour or sugar.

memory enhancers

❶ The most important meal of the day is breakfast so it should comprise of high-protein food (eggs, meat, dairy, beans) and a high-fibre starch (wholewheat bread or high fibre cereal). This can improve memory and enhance alertness.

❷ Have eggs. A study reveals that the choline found in eggs may be beneficial in the production of the neurotransmitter acetylcholine. Low levels of acetylcholine are associated with Alzheimer's disease, so increasing the dietary intake may slow down age-related memory loss.

❸ Omega-3 fatty acids are healthy. Many studies have found the health benefits of omega-3 fatty acids in memory-building. Foods high in omega-3 fatty acids will support brain function as well as help prevent clogging of arteries which is good not only for the heart but for the blood flow to the brain. The best sources are fatty fish like salmon, mackerel, lake trout, herring, sardines, tuna, flax seed oil, canola oil, soybean oil, flax seeds and walnuts.

❹ Drink water. If we are what we eat, then wouldn't we be what we drink as well? Our bodies are composed of 60% water and our brain is about 75% water, so it is obvious that water can impact our health. While there is no research to show that drinking water improves our memory, it has been shown that even a small amount of dehydration leads to confusion and problems with memory. In other words, don't wait to drink water.

have antioxidants

Antioxidants are substances that may protect the cells against the effects of free radicals. Free radicals are molecules produced when the body breaks down food, or by environmental exposures like tobacco smoke and radiation. Antioxidants act as 'free radical scavengers' and hence prevent and repair damage done by these free radicals. Health problems such as diabetes and heart disease are all contributions of oxidative damage. Nutritionists say that 5 servings of fruits and vegetables reduce the risk of stroke by 25 percent. Antioxidants may also enhance the immune system.

antioxidants and their sources

❶ Vitamin A and Beta-carotene: carrots, squash, broccoli, sweet potatoes, kale, tomatoes, peaches and apricots (all bright-coloured fruits and vegetables!).

❷ Lutein: dark green vegetables such as kale, broccoli, kiwi, Brussels sprout and spinach.

❸ Lycopene: tomato and its products, watermelon.

❹ Selenium: fish, shellfish, red meat, grains, eggs, chicken and garlic.

❺ Vitamin C: citrus fruits like oranges and lime etc, green capsicums, broccoli, green leafy vegetables, strawberries and tomato.

❻ Vitamin E: nuts and seeds, whole grains, green leafy vegetables, vegetable oil and liver oil.

❼ Lignin: flax seeds, rye, oatmeal, barley.

maintain a healthy glowing skin

Eating a variety of healthy foods and drinking plenty of water so that the skin stays hydrated should help most people improve the appearance of their skin.

what helps keep the skin healthy

❶ One of the most important components of skin health is Vitamin A. One of the best sources of Vitamin A are low-fat dairy products. Low-fat yogurt is not only high in Vitamin A, but also in acidophilus, the live bacteria that is good for intestinal health. Anything that helps keep digestion normal, any live bacteria or enzymes, is also going to be reflected in healthy-looking skin.

❷ Vitamin E is a principal fat-soluble antioxidant vitamin in the body. It protects cellular membranes, lipoproteins and other oily structures. Skin is high in unsaturated fatty acids and can benefit from vitamin E protection, both oral and topical.

❸ Flavonoids, found in grapes and green tea, are good for the skin. They are a diverse group of plant pigments with antioxidant properties. These substances are responsible for colour in many fruits, vegetables and flowers.

❹ It is found that our dietary habits are responsible for making the skin unhealthy. The biggest offenders are fats and carbohydrates. Foods high in fat include red meat, dark-meat poultry, full-fat dairy, butter, lard and oils. Avoid foods that are cooked with a lot of fat, including fried foods, desserts, cream-based gravies and sauces and fast foods. Remember that fat is necessary in the diet, but excessive fat/saturated/trans-fats are not healthy. Instead, eat more healthy fat like mustard oil, groundnut oil, and olive oil and omega-3-rich fats found in fatty fish, walnuts and flax seeds.

❺ It is not enough to say "reduce carbohydrates for better skin" because one should not reduce consumption of fruit and vegetables; instead one should increase consumption of these foods. Reduce the amount of processed carbohydrates such as white bread and white rice. Avoid sugar-filled foods like cookies, cakes, pastries, and candy.

❻ Refrain from excessive alcohol intake, which is dehydrating, and make sure to drink plenty of water.

❼ Stop smoking. Tobacco limits blood supply to the skin.

❽ Get plenty of sleep for cell rejuvenation takes place in sleep and gives the skin sun protection at all times.

have a healthy heart

To lower the risk of heart disease, choose foods carefully:

❶ Cut down on fats. Some fats are more likely to cause heart disease e.g., saturated fats and trans-fats. These fats are usually found in foods from animals, such as meat, milk, cheese and butter. They also are found in foods with palm and coconut oils. Eat less of these foods.

❷ Reduce salt. Low salt (sodium) can help lower blood pressure. This can help reduce the risk of heart disease. Sodium is something we need in our diets, but most of us eat too much of it. Avoid adding salt to foods at the table.

❸ Stick to low calorie foods. When we eat more calories than we need, we gain weight. Being overweight can cause heart disease. When we eat fewer calories than we need, we lose weight.

❹ Incorporate more fibrous foods. Eating fibre from fruits, vegetables and grains may help lower risk of heart disease.

❺ Maintain or improve body-weight.

have power foods for muscular strength

The muscles of the body are the root of all the calorie burning and physical fitness. The strength of these muscles is quickly becoming a major focus of fitness gurus. It is important to build muscular strength in order to increase overall body fitness. In recent years, more focus has been placed on the importance of muscular strength and weight training exercises as a part of a balanced fitness routine. When seeking to build muscular strength, there is only one real way and that is to work the muscle.

understanding power foods

Make them a large part of the daily diet. As one eats more of these foods, the better the body will be able to increase lean muscle mass and will also avoid storing fat. Power foods help in muscle-building, weight-loss, strengthening of bones, keeping a check on blood pressure, build immunity and resistance power and safeguard against heart disease.

Incorporate two or three of these foods into each of the three major daily meals and at least one of them into each of the three daily snacks. Diversify the foods at every meal to get a combination of protein, carbohydrates and fat. Make sure to sneak in a little bit of protein into each snack.

power foods

INGREDIENT	SUPER POWERS	AVAILABLE NUTRIENTS	IMPOSTERS
Cereals: Instant oatmeal, unsweetened, unflavoured	Boosts energy, reduces cholesterol, maintains blood-sugar levels	Complex carbohydrates and fibre	Sugary cereals
Whole-grain breads and cereals	Prevents body from storing fat	Fibre, protein, thiamine, riboflavin, niacin, zinc, Vitamin E, calcium, magnesium, potassium	Processed bakery products like white bread, doughnuts
Dals and pulses including soybeans, chickpeas, kidney beans, lima beans	Builds muscle, helps burn fat, regulates digestion	Fibre, protein, iron, folate	Refried beans, which are high in saturated fats; baked beans, which are high in sugar
Spinach and other green vegetables	Neutralizes free radicals	Vitamins including A, C and K; folate; beta-carotene; minerals including calcium and magnesium; fibre	None, as long as not deep-fried or smothered in fatty cheese sauces
Dairy Products: fat-free or low-fat milk, yogurt, cheese, cottage cheese	Builds strong bones, facilitates weight loss	Calcium, Vitamins A and B12, riboflavin, phosphorus, potassium	Whole milk, frozen yogurt
Eggs	Builds muscle, burns fat	Protein, Vitamins A and B12	
Turkey and other lean meats, lean steak, chicken, fish	Builds muscle, improves the immune system	Protein, iron, zinc, omega-3 fatty acids (fish), Vitamins B6 (chicken and fish) and B12, phosphorus, potassium	Sausage, bacon, cured meats, ham, fatty cuts of steak like T-bone and ribs
Nuts and oil seeds, almonds (with skin)	Builds muscle, fights food cravings	Protein, monounsaturated fats, Vitamin E, folate (in peanuts), fibre, magnesium, phosphorus	Salted or smoked nuts. High sodium spikes blood pressure
Fats and oils Peanut Butter	Boosts testosterone, builds muscle, burns fat	Protein, monounsaturated fat, Vitamin E, niacin, magnesium	Mass-produced sugary and trans-fatty peanut butter
Olive Oil	Lowers cholesterol, boosts the immune system	Monounsaturated fat, Vitamin E	Other vegetable and hydrogenated vegetable oils, trans-fatty acids, margarine

achaari gobhi

Ingredients

1 medium cauliflower
1½ tablespoons mustard oil
½ teaspoon mustard seeds
½ teaspoon cumin seeds
¼ teaspoon fenugreek seeds
½ teaspoon fennel seeds
¼ teaspoon onion seeds
1 teaspoon coriander seeds, crushed
¼ teaspoon asafoetida
1 medium onion, chopped
1 teaspoon ginger paste
1 teaspoon garlic paste
3 green chillies, chopped
Salt to taste
½ teaspoon turmeric powder
¾ cup skimmed milk yogurt

Method

❶ Separate the cauliflower into large florets.

❷ Heat the mustard oil to smoking point in a non-stick *kadai*; add the mustard seeds, cumin seeds, fenugreek seeds, fennel seeds, onion seeds, crushed coriander seeds and asafoetida, and sauté till they begin to change colour.

❸ Add the onion and sauté till translucent. Add the ginger paste, garlic paste and green chillies and sauté till the onion turns light brown.

❹ Add the cauliflower and salt and sauté over medium heat till brown.

❺ Add the turmeric powder and one cup of water and cook, covered, for ten to fifteen minutes, or till cooked.

❻ Add the yogurt and continue to cook till the water evaporates and the gravy coats the cauliflower.

❼ Serve hot.

Cauliflower belongs to the cruciferous family. These vegetables are high in water content and fibre and low in calories and fat. The various spices in this recipe are anti-microbial in nature, so they help to prevent infections in the body.

aloo ka
rassawala shaak

Ingredients

4 medium potatoes, boiled
and cut into ½-inch pieces
1 cup skimmed milk yogurt
1 tablespoon gram flour
Salt to taste
¼ teaspoon turmeric powder
1 tablespoon ghee
½ teaspoon cumin seeds
A pinch of asafoetida
7-8 curry leaves
½ inch ginger, chopped
2 green chillies, chopped
¼ teaspoon red chilli powder
½ teaspoon *garam masala* powder

Method

❶ Whisk the yogurt with the gram flour, salt and turmeric powder. Add three-fourth cup of water and mix well.

❷ Heat the ghee in a non-stick pan. Add the cumin seeds and when they begin to change colour, add the asafoetida, curry leaves, ginger and green chillies. Sauté for a minute.

❸ Add the chilli powder and the yogurt mixture and mix well.

❹ Add the potatoes and cook stirring continuously. Once the mixture comes to a boil, reduce heat and simmer for five to six minutes till the potatoes are soft.

❺ Garnish with *garam masala* powder and serve hot.

Unexpected guests? Well, they will enjoy this dish of potatoes cooked in tangy yogurt. Just serve it with hot *roti*! Curry leaves add their unique flavour.

baghare baingan

Ingredients

250 grams small brinjals
2 medium onions, quartered
1½ teaspoons coriander seeds
1½ tablespoons sesame seeds
2 tablespoons peanuts
½ teaspoon cumin seeds
¾ teaspoon poppy seeds
1 tablespoon grated dried coconut
A pinch of fenugreek seeds
1 inch ginger, roughly chopped
6-8 garlic cloves, roughly chopped
Salt to taste
A pinch of turmeric powder
½ teaspoon red chilli powder
½ teaspoon grated jaggery or sugar
2 tablespoons tamarind pulp
2 tablespoons olive oil
1 sprig curry leaves

Method

❶ Wash the brinjals and slit lengthways into four, with the quarters held together at the stalk.

❷ Dry-roast the onions on a *tawa* till they turn soft and pale gold.

❸ Dry-roast the coriander seeds, sesame seeds, peanuts, cumin seeds, poppy seeds, dried coconut and fenugreek seeds all together till fragrant and they begin to change colour.

❹ Grind together the roasted onions, roasted spices, ginger, garlic, salt, turmeric powder, chilli powder and jaggery or sugar to a very fine paste. Add the tamarind pulp and mix well. Stuff the slit brinjals with some *masala* and reserve the rest.

❺ Heat the oil in a non-stick *kadai*, add the curry leaves and sauté for a minute. Add the stuffed brinjals and sauté for about ten minutes. Add the reserved *masala* and mix gently. Add two cups of water, cover and cook over low heat till the brinjals are completely cooked and the oil rises to the surface. Serve hot.

This is a traditional rich vegetarian preparation and its combination of spices is very representative of the Hyderabadi culture. In earlier times, travellers carried it because of its long shelf-life. It is versatile enough to taste good with rice as well as *chapati*.

gatta curry

Ingredients

Gatta
2½ cups gram flour, sifted
3 tablespoons skimmed milk yogurt
½ teaspoon cumin seeds
½ teaspoon red chilli powder
½ teaspoon turmeric powder
Salt to taste
A pinch of soda bicarbonate

Gravy
2 medium onions
½ inch ginger
1½ cups skimmed milk yogurt
1 teaspoon red chilli powder
2 teaspoons coriander powder
½ teaspoon turmeric powder
1 teaspoon cumin seeds
A pinch of asafoetida
Salt to taste
½ teaspoon *garam masala* powder
2 tablespoons chopped fresh coriander

Method

❶ Mix all the ingredients for the *gatta*. Add sufficient water to make a stiff dough. Divide into six equal portions. Roll into cylindrical shapes.

❷ Cook in five cups of boiling hot water for ten to fifteen minutes. Drain and reserve the water for the gravy. Cut the *gattas* diagonally into one-inch pieces.

❸ Roughly chop the onions and boil them in half a cup of water. Cool and grind with the ginger to a fine paste.

❹ Whisk the yogurt with chilli powder, coriander powder and turmeric powder.

❺ Heat a non-stick pan. Add the cumin seeds and asafoetida. Roast on low heat until the cumin seeds start to change colour.

❻ Add the onion paste and cook on low heat till light pink in colour.

❼ Add the yogurt mixture and continue to cook on low heat for five minutes.

❽ Add the *gattas* and one cup of the reserved water in which the *gattas* were boiled. Cook on low heat till the gravy thickens. Add the *garam masala* powder and adjust salt.

❾ Garnish with the fresh coriander and serve hot.

Gram flour is an excellent food for those who have high energy and protein requirements. It is also rich in iron and phosphorus.

capsicum kayras

Ingredients

5-6 medium green capsicums,
cut into 1-inch pieces
2 medium potatoes, peeled
and cut into 1-inch cubes
1½ tablespoons rice bran oil
½ teaspoon mustard seeds
A pinch of asafoetida
½ cup peanuts
¼ teaspoon turmeric powder
Salt to taste
1½ tablespoons grated jaggery

Masala
¼ cup grated coconut
1 tablespoon melon seeds
3 tablespoons sesame seeds
2 tablespoons split Bengal gram
2 tablespoons coriander seeds
¼ teaspoon fenugreek seeds
4-5 dried red chillies (preferably *Bedgi*)
2 tablespoons tamarind pulp

Method

❶ For the *masala*, dry-roast the coconut, melon seeds and sesame seeds separately. Heat half a tablespoon of oil in a pan; add the split Bengal gram, coriander seeds, fenugreek seeds and red chillies and sauté till fragrant. Grind the spices with the roasted coconut, sesame seeds, melon seeds, tamarind pulp and three-fourth cup of water to a fine paste.

❷ Heat the remaining oil in a pan and add the mustard seeds. When they begin to splutter, add the asafoetida, stir and add the peanuts; sauté for three to four minutes.

❸ Add the potatoes, turmeric powder, salt and jaggery. Stir, cover and cook on low heat for five minutes. Add the capsicums, stir and cook till the vegetables are half-done.

❹ Add the ground paste, one-and-a-half cups of water and simmer for three to four minutes.

❺ Serve hot.

Capsicum is rich in Vitamin C and fibre, whereas melon seeds are a good source of potassium and omega-3 fatty acids. Sesame seeds are 25 per cent protein and are especially rich in methionine and tryptophan, often not present in adequate quantities in many plant proteins.

makai palak

Ingredients

½ cup corn kernels boiled
2 bunches (700 grams) fresh spinach, chopped
2 medium onions, chopped
1 inch ginger, grated
2 green chillies, chopped
A pinch of turmeric powder
½ teaspoon red chilli powder
½ teaspoon dried mango powder
¼ cup skimmed milk yogurt
Salt to taste
½ teaspoon *garam masala* powder
¼ teaspoon dried fenugreek leaves, powdered
1 inch ginger, cut into thin strips

Method

❶ Blanch the spinach, drain and purée in a blender.

❷ Heat a non-stick pan and roast the onions, ginger and green chillies for two to three minutes.

❸ Add the turmeric, chilli and dried mango powders. Add one-fourth cup of water. Mix well and simmer for one to two minutes.

❹ Add the yogurt and mix well. Add the spinach purée, boiled corn and salt and cook for two minutes.

❺ Add the *garam masala* powder and powdered dried fenugreek leaves and remove from heat.

❻ Garnish with the ginger strips and serve hot with *roti*.

Spinach is high in calcium, iron and Vitamins A and C. It is a valuable source of folic acid for pregnant and lactating women. Corn provides the carbohydrates and fibre.

chorchori

Ingredients

125 grams cauliflower,
separated into small florets
2 medium potatoes, diced
1 medium sweet potato, diced
100 grams pumpkin, diced
1 medium long brinjal, diced
6-8 French beans,
cut into ½-inch pieces
6-8 spinach leaves, shredded
1 tablespoon mustard oil
1½ teaspoons *panch phoron*
½ teaspoon red chilli powder
¼ teaspoon turmeric powder
2 green chillies, slit
½ teaspoon sugar
Salt to taste

Method

❶ Heat the mustard oil in a non-stick pan until it reaches smoking point. Remove from heat, cool and heat the oil again on medium heat.

❷ Add the *panch phoron* and when the seeds begin to splutter, add the chilli powder, stirring briefly.

❸ Stir in the prepared vegetables, followed by the turmeric powder, green chillies, sugar and salt.

❹ Reduce the heat, cover and cook for eight to ten minutes, stirring occasionally or until the potatoes are cooked.

❺ Uncover and stir-fry for one minute and or until the *chorchori* is dry.

Chef's Tip: Panch phoron, also known as Bengali five-spice, can be bought ready-made, but it can be easily made at home. Mix together equal quantities of mustard seeds, cumin seeds, fenugreek seeds, fennel seeds and onion seeds.

There is a story behind this mixed vegetable dish. In many Bengali households, shopping for fresh vegetables was the duty of the man of the house. And it was done once a week on his day off from work. By the end of the week, the lady of the house was left with bits of all the various vegetables. Hence, this delicious and nutritious innovation! Onion seeds, if consumed regularly, can help relieve gas and flatulence as well as strengthen stomach muscles.

chutneywale aloo

Ingredients

40 baby potatoes
½ teaspoon turmeric powder
Salt to taste
1 cup fresh coriander, roughly chopped
¼ cup fresh mint, coarsely shredded
10-12 green chillies, roughly chopped
4-6 garlic cloves, roughly chopped
2 inches ginger, roughly chopped
4 teaspoons lemon juice
2 teaspoons cumin seeds
2 teaspoons coriander powder
1 teaspoon cumin powder
½ cup skimmed milk yogurt
1 teaspoon sesame seeds, toasted

Method

❶ Parboil the potatoes with salt and one-fourth teaspoon of turmeric powder. Drain, cool and halve without peeling.

❷ For the chutney, grind together the fresh coriander, fresh mint, green chillies, garlic and ginger along with salt and lemon juice to a fine paste.

❸ Heat a non-stick pan and dry-roast the cumin seeds till fragrant. Add the halved potatoes, coriander powder, cumin powder and remaining turmeric powder and mix. Add half a cup of water, cover and cook on low heat till the potatoes are done.

❹ Add the chutney, half a cup of water and mix. Adjust the salt and simmer for three to four minutes or till the gravy has thickened. Add the yogurt and stir. Cook till it comes to a boil and take it off the heat.

❺ Sprinkle the toasted sesame seeds and serve hot.

Fresh mint has many properties, the most popular one being an agent that relieves gastric discomfort! Mint is also a good appetiser. Fresh coriander, which is aromatic and contains essential oils, is an excellent appetiser and helps in proper secretion of enzymes and digestive juices in the stomach.

pyaaz ki tarkari

Ingredients

8 medium onions, chopped
1½ tablespoons rice bran oil
1 teaspoon ginger paste
1 teaspoon garlic paste
Salt to taste
½ teaspoon turmeric powder
1 teaspoon red chilli powder
8 spring onions, quartered
2 tablespoons tamarind pulp
5 stalks spring onion greens, chopped

Method

❶ Heat the oil in a non-stick *kadai*; add the onions and sauté till golden.

❷ Add the ginger paste and garlic paste and sauté for one minute.

❸ Add the salt, turmeric and chilli powders, spring onions and one-third cup of water. When the mixture begins to boil, lower the heat and simmer for two to three minutes.

❹ Stir in the tamarind pulp and cook for one minute.

❺ Serve hot, garnished with the spring onion greens.

Onions have a lot of good things going for them: they are low-calorie, cholesterol and sodium-free. Yet, they usually play a supporting role. In this dish, however, the onion is a star performer! Serve with hot *khichdi*.

nadur palak

Ingredients

250 grams lotus root (*nadur*)
2 bunches fresh spinach leaves, chopped
¼ teaspoon asafoetida
2 tablespoons rice bran oil
Salt to taste
1 teaspoon red chilli powder
½ teaspoon turmeric powder
1 teaspoon dried ginger powder
½ teaspoon *garam masala* powder

Method

❶ Scrape the lotus root well. Cut into thick round slices and wash thoroughly. Mix the asafoetida with one tablespoon of water.

❷ Heat the oil in a pressure cooker and stir-fry the lotus roots for five minutes. Add the asafoetida mixture, salt and spinach.

❸ Add half a cup of water, seal the cooker with the lid and cook over medium heat till the pressure is released three times (three whistles).

❹ Remove the lid when the pressure has reduced completely. Stir in the chilli, turmeric and dried ginger powders. Simmer till almost all the water has dried up.

❺ Sprinkle the *garam masala* powder and remove from heat. Serve hot.

Nadur Palak is an everyday recipe in a Kashmiri home but where lotus root is not available easily it becomes a delicacy. Choose slim, pinkish lotus roots and clean them thoroughly as they are usually muddy. Lotus root is low in saturated fats and cholesterol, high in dietary fibre, Vitamins C and B, potassium and phosphorus.

mirchi ka salan

Ingredients

18-20 big green chillies
2 tablespoons sesame seeds
1 tablespoon coriander seeds
1 teaspoon cumin seeds
½ cup roasted peanuts
2 dried red chillies, broken
1 inch ginger, chopped
6-8 garlic cloves
1½ tablespoons oil
1 teaspoon mustard seeds
8-10 curry leaves
1 medium onion, grated
1 teaspoon turmeric powder
2 tablespoons tamarind pulp
Salt to taste

Method

❶ Wash, wipe and slit the green chillies lengthways without cutting through.

❷ Dry-roast the sesame, coriander and cumin seeds. Cool and grind to a paste along with the roasted peanuts, red chillies, ginger and garlic.

❸ Heat the oil in a non-stick pan and add the mustard seeds. Once they splutter add the curry leaves. Sauté for half a minute and add the onion. Sauté, stirring continuously, till the onion is light golden brown.

❹ Add the turmeric powder and mix well. Add the *masala* paste and cook for three minutes, stirring constantly. Add the chillies and continue to sauté for further two minutes

❺ Stir in one-and-a-half cups of water and bring it to a boil. Reduce the heat and cook for ten minutes. Add the tamarind pulp (dissolved in half a cup of water, if it is too thick).

❻ Add the salt and cook on low heat for eight to ten minutes.

In Hyderabad, *Mirchi ka Salan* is traditionally served as an accompaniment to *biryanis*. Some people like to add grated coconut to the *masala* paste, but I prefer *Mirchi ka Salan* without coconut. This gravy is referred to as *Tili* (*Til-Sesame*) *aur Falli* (*Moongphali*-Peanuts).

gwar ki sabzi

Ingredients

1½ cups dried cluster beans
1 tablespoon mustard oil
1 bay leaf
½ teaspoon cumin seeds
5-6 dried red chillies, broken
A pinch of asafoetida
½ teaspoon mustard powder
Salt to taste
3 tablespoons skimmed milk yogurt, whisked
1 teaspoon red chilli powder
½ teaspoon turmeric powder
1 tablespoon *garam masala* powder
½ teaspoon dried mango powder
1 teaspoon coriander powder
½ teaspoon sugar
2-3 pieces dried mango, soaked

Method

❶ Soak the cluster beans in four cups of water for one hour. Drain.

❷ Heat the mustard oil in a non-stick pan. Stir in the bay leaf, cumin seeds, red chillies, asafoetida and mustard powder.

❸ Add the soaked beans and salt. Mix well and stir in the yogurt.

❹ Mix together all the spice powders with a little water and add to the vegetable. Add the dried mango pieces and cook till dry.

❺ Serve hot.

Cluster beans or *gwar* are a good source of dietary fibre. The extract from the beans called *gwar gum* is known to lower cholesterol levels.

karele ka salan

Ingredients

350 grams bitter gourd
½ teaspoon turmeric powder
Salt to taste
2 tablespoons rice bran oil
2 small onions, chopped
1 inch ginger, chopped
6 garlic cloves, chopped
1 tablespoon coriander seeds
¾ teaspoon cumin seeds
1½ tablespoons sesame seeds
2 tablespoons peanuts
3 dried red chillies, broken
2 tablespoons tamarind pulp
1½ teaspoons grated jaggery
¼ teaspoon garam masala powder
2 tablespoons chopped fresh coriander

Method

❶ Lightly scrape the skin off the bitter gourds. Slit them lengthways on one side without cutting through and remove the seeds and pulp. Rub half the turmeric powder and salt into the bitter gourds and set aside for fifteen to twenty minutes. Wash under running water, drain well and set aside.

❷ Heat half a tablespoon of oil in a non-stick pan and lightly roast the onions, ginger, garlic, coriander seeds, cumin seeds, sesame seeds, peanuts and dried red chillies. Cool and grind to a fine paste.

❸ Mix the paste with the tamarind pulp, remaining turmeric powder, jaggery and garam masala powder.

❹ Stuff the bitter gourds with the masala and tie with a string. Reserve the remaining masala.

❺ Heat the remaining oil in a non-stick pan and place the bitter gourds in it one by one. Shallow-fry for five minutes, turning them from time to time to brown evenly on all sides.

❻ Add the remaining masala and add half a cup of water, cover and cook till the bitter gourds are tender.

❼ Stir gently to coat with the masala. Remove from heat.
❽ Garnish with the fresh coriander and serve hot.

The bitter gourds are cooked with the traditional, tasty tilli-phalli Hyderabadi combination. Bitter gourd is recommended for everyone as it is valued for its nutritional properties. It is high in insoluble fibre and is known to reduce blood sugar levels so can be recommended to diabetics.

ekadashi jeera aloo

Ingredients

500 grams baby potatoes, parboiled
and halved
1 teaspoon cumin seeds
2 tablespoons rice bran oil
15-18 curry leaves
2 green chillies, slit
Rock salt to taste
1½ teaspoons sugar
2 tablespoons lemon juice
2 tablespoons chopped fresh coriander
1½ tablespoons grated coconut

Method

❶ Heat the oil in a non-stick *kadai*; add the cumin seeds, curry leaves and green chillies and sauté till they begin to change colour.

❷ Add the potatoes and rock salt and sauté over medium heat for two minutes. Cover and cook over low heat till the potatoes are completely done and well- browned.

❸ Add the sugar, lemon juice, fresh coriander and coconut. Toss well to mix.
❹ Serve hot.

Potatoes have been used specifically because they provide the energy necessary during a fast. Rock salt has cooling properties and its own special taste.

masaledaar karele

Ingredients

12 medium (750 grams) bitter gourds
Salt to taste
2 teaspoons coriander powder
2 teaspoons cumin powder
¾ teaspoon turmeric powder
1½ tablespoons dried mango powder
¾ tablespoon red chilli powder
½ tablespoon *garam masala* powder
3½ tablespoons fennel seeds
3 tablespoons oil
2 large onions, finely chopped
1 tablespoon sugar

Method

❶ Scrape the bitter gourds; make a slit on one side and remove the seeds. Rub the salt over and inside the bitter gourds and set aside for half an hour. Squeeze lightly and wash under running water. Wipe dry.

❷ Dry-roast all the *masala* powders one by one on low heat till fragrant. Dry-roast the fennel seeds and grind coarsely. Mix all the powders together.

❸ Heat one tablespoon of oil in a non-stick pan and sauté the onions till golden. Remove from the heat and add the *masala* powders, salt and sugar.

❹ Fill the *masala* mixture into the slits of the bitter gourds.

❺ Heat the remaining oil in a wide non-stick pan. Neatly arrange the bitter gourds on the pan. Cover with a tight lid and cook over low heat till done.

❻ Uncover and sauté the gourds till lightly browned.

❼ Serve hot.

Even those who do not like bitter gourds might just enjoy this recipe, for the spicy stuffing masks the bitterness to a great extent. Bitter gourds are known for their excellent nutritive value and their role in lowering the blood sugar levels. They are also high in fibre.

masaledaar tofu bhurji

Ingredients

300 grams tofu
1½ teaspoons olive oil
1 teaspoon cumin seeds
2 medium onions, chopped
1 inch ginger, chopped
2 green chillies, chopped
½ teaspoon turmeric powder
1 teaspoon red chilli powder
1 tablespoon coriander powder
1 teaspoon cumin powder
2 medium tomatoes, chopped
2 medium green capsicums,
seeded and chopped
Salt to taste
¼ cup chopped fresh coriander

Method

❶ Drain the tofu and crumble it into small pieces.

❷ Heat the oil in a non-stick pan and add the cumin seeds. When they begin to change colour, add the onions, ginger and green chillies. Stir-fry till the onions becomes translucent.

❸ Mix the turmeric, chilli, coriander and cumin powders in half a cup of water and add to the pan. Cook on medium heat for half a minute, stirring continuously.

❹ Add the tomatoes and cook on high heat for two minutes, stirring continuously. Stir in the crumbled tofu, capsicums and salt to taste. Mix well.

❺ Lower the heat and cook for two to three minutes, tossing frequently to prevent the tofu from sticking to the pan.

❻ Sprinkle the fresh coriander on top and serve.

Soyabean curd or tofu has a bland taste and cheese-like appearance. It is commonly used in Oriental cooking. Tofu is rich in protein, polyunsaturated fats, B complex vitamins and iron. Tofu resembles *paneer* in texture but is lower in fat.

doodhi paneer
ka sukha salan

Ingredients

600 grams bottle gourd, cut into ¾-inch diamonds

200 grams cottage cheese, cut into ¾-inch diamonds

1 medium red capsicum, cut into ¾-inch diamonds

1 medium yellow capsicum, cut into ¾-inch diamonds

1 medium green capsicum, cut into ¾-inch diamonds

2 tablespoons grated dried coconut

1 tablespoon peanuts

1 teaspoon sesame seeds

1 lemon-sized ball of tamarind

3 tablespoons rice bran oil

1 medium onion, sliced

¼ teaspoon cumin seeds

¼ teaspoon fenugreek seeds

¼ teaspoon fennel seeds

¼ teaspoon onion seeds

¼ teaspoon mustard seeds

8 curry leaves

2 teaspoons ginger-garlic paste

4 green chillies, chopped

1 teaspoon coriander powder

½ teaspoon cumin powder

¼ teaspoon turmeric powder

½ teaspoon red chilli powder

Salt to taste

½ teaspoon *garam masala* powder

1 tablespoon chopped fresh coriander

Method

❶ Dry-roast the coconut, peanuts and sesame seeds.
Cool and grind to a fine paste. Soak the tamarind for
thirty minutes in warm water, squeeze and strain
the pulp.

❷ Heat half the oil in a non-stick *kadai* and sauté
the onions till golden brown. Drain on absorbent paper.

❸ Heat the remaining oil in another pan. Add the cumin
seeds, fenugreek seeds, fennel seeds, onion seeds and
mustard seeds. Once they begin to splutter add the curry
leaves and ginger-garlic paste. Sauté till the raw flavours
disappear. Add the green chillies and *doodhi* and sauté
for four to five minutes. Add the capsicums and cook,
covered for ten to fifteen minutes.

❹ Add the coriander powder, cumin powder, turmeric
powder and red chilli powder. Sauté for three to four
minutes. Add the sautéed onions and salt. Stir-fry for
three to four minutes. Add the coconut-peanut-sesame
paste and stir-fry until the oil separates. Stir in the
tamarind pulp. Add the *paneer* and toss well to coat with
the spices. Sprinkle the *garam masala* powder and fresh
coriander. Stir and remove from heat. Serve hot with *roti*.

The coconut *masala* makes this dish rather special.
Bottle gourd is low in calories and fat and rich in
insoluble fibre. It is proven to be the best for lowering
cholesterol and cleansing the intestines.

gobhi matar

Ingredients

1 medium cauliflower, separated
into florets
1 cup shelled green peas
1 tablespoon rice bran oil
1 teaspoon cumin seeds
1 teaspoon ginger paste
1 teaspoon garlic paste
2 teaspoons coriander powder
½ teaspoon red chilli powder
½ teaspoon turmeric powder
¼ cup tomato purée
Salt to taste
1 teaspoon *garam masala* powder
½ teaspoon dried mango powder
1 green chilli, slit
1 tablespoon chopped fresh coriander

Method

❶ Heat the oil in a non-stick *kadai* and add the cumin seeds. When they begin to change colour add the ginger paste and garlic paste. Sauté for half a minute.

❷ Add the coriander powder, chilli powder and turmeric powder. Sauté for another half a minute.

❸ Add the cauliflower florets, green peas, half a cup of water and tomato purée. Add the salt and mix. Cover and cook for eight to ten minutes, stirring occasionally.

❹ Add the *garam masala* powder and dried mango powder and mix.

❺ Garnish with the green chilli and fresh coriander and serve hot.

When I was a child, heaven was hot *Gobhi Matar* with thick *paranthas* and fresh *dahi* on cold winter afternoons. Green peas are rich in protein and carbohydrates but low in fats. They provide water soluble fibre, Vitamins A, C and also thiamine (vitamin B1) and iron. Being fibrous they promote good intestinal health. Thiamine is essential for nerve function.

paneer jhalfrezi

Ingredients

300 grams skimmed milk cottage cheese cut into 1-inch fingers
2 medium tomatoes, halved and seeded
2 medium green capsicums, halved and seeded
2 medium onions, thickly sliced
1 tablespoon olive oil
1 teaspoon cumin seeds
2 dried red chillies, halved
1 inch ginger, cut into thin strips
1-2 green chillies, chopped
1 teaspoon red chilli powder
½ teaspoon turmeric powder
Salt to taste
1½ tablespoons vinegar
1 teaspoon *garam masala* powder
1 tablespoon chopped fresh coriander

Method

❶ Cut the tomatoes and capsicums into thick slices. Separate the layers of the sliced onions.

❷ Heat the oil in a non-stick *kadai*. Add the cumin seeds. When they change colour add the red chillies, ginger strips, green chillies and onions. Sauté for thirty seconds.

❸ Stir in the chilli and turmeric powders. Add the capsicums and cook for two-three minutes. Add the cottage cheese and toss. Add the salt and vinegar and cook for two-three minutes. Stir in the tomato pieces and *garam masala* and cook for two minutes.

❹ Garnish with the fresh coriander and serve hot.

This tasty and colourful dish can be prepared in just a few minutes. This is a family favourite and cooked at home at least once a week. Using skimmed milk cottage cheese instead of whole milk cottage cheese is a healthier alternative. The protein content is not altered... only the fat content is reduced which is advisable for health. Serve with *roti*.

kaju khumb makhana

Ingredients

½ cup whole cashew nuts, soaked
500 grams fresh button mushrooms
2 cups puffed lotus seeds (*makhana*)
1 tablespoon oil
½ cup skimmed milk yogurt
1 tablespoon coriander powder
1½ teaspoons red chilli powder
1 teaspoon turmeric powder
1 tablespoon ghee
1 teaspoon cumin seeds
3 medium onions, chopped
2 teaspoons ginger paste
2 teaspoons garlic paste
2 teaspoons black pepper powder
1½ cups fresh tomato purée
Salt to taste
1 teaspoon *garam masala* powder
1 tablespoon honey (optional)
1 tablespoon lemon juice
2 tablespoons chopped fresh coriander

Method

❶ Remove the stalks of the mushrooms, clean and boil until three-fourth cooked. Drain and set aside.

❷ Heat the oil a non-stick *kadai* and stir-fry the puffed lotus seeds for half a minute. Drain and soak in a bowl of water.

❸ Place the yogurt in a bowl and whisk with the coriander, chilli and turmeric powders.

❹ Heat the ghee in another non-stick pan, add the cumin seeds and when they begin to change colour add the onions and sauté until translucent.

❺ Add the ginger paste and garlic paste and sauté for five minutes. Add the pepper powder and sauté for two minutes.

❻ Add the mushrooms and continue to sauté for five minutes.

❼ Add the yogurt mixture and cook till the oil rises to the surface.

❽ Add the tomato purée and salt and sauté till the oil rises to the surface again.

❾ Add two-and-a-half cups of water and bring to a boil, reduce heat and add the cashew nuts and puffed lotus seeds. Cover and simmer, stirring occasionally, for eight to ten minutes.

❿ Sprinkle the *garam masala* powder and mix. Add the honey and lemon juice and mix well. Adjust the seasoning.

⓫ Garnish with the fresh coriander and serve with the *roti*.

Makhana are puffed lotus seeds. They are offered in religious ceremonies and are eaten during fasts. Lotus seeds have medicinal properties and are beneficial in cardiovascular diseases, improve blood circulation and post-natal care. *Makhana* are also rich in protein and can be given to growing children.

healthy diet for every stage in life

At every stage of life, from infancy to old age, as you grow and develop, the nutritional requirements also change. There are healthy foods that can keep you fit at every stage.

infancy

Infancy is the period between birth to one year when rapid growth takes place. The newborn baby should be fed only breast milk for the first six months, as breast milk provides complete nutrition. The first milk or colostrum is vital and should be fed to the baby without fail. This special milk is yellow to orange in colour, thick and sticky. It is low in fat, and high in carbohydrates, protein and antibodies to help keep the baby healthy.

Colostrum is extremely easy to digest and is therefore the perfect first food for the baby. It is low in volume (measurable in teaspoons), but high in concentrated nutrition for the newborn. Colostrum has a laxative effect, helping the baby pass its early stools, getting rid of the excess bilirubin and helping to prevent jaundice. Even honey and water are not advisable till six months of age. Breast milk is sufficient to meet the baby's needs.

Infants require 80-140 kcal/kg body weight. Seventy per cent of the calories are fulfilled by breast milk alone and the rest of calories can be supplemented through top foods after the sixth month. After the sixth month, the need for calories and protein increases due to skeletal and muscular growth so top feeding (weaning) can be started. The baby especially needs Essential Fatty Acids (EFA) as a deficiency can lead to skin lesions, diarrhoea and growth retardation. Breast milk and cow's milk contain the EFAs required.

food for weaning

Milk: Milk diluted in the proportion 2:1 is recommended. 225 ml of milk per feed is ideal. Sugar can be added to improve the taste and increase calorific value.

Fresh fruit juice: Breast milk lacks in Vitamin C, so juicy citrus fruits are recommended. Dilute the fresh juice in the proportion 1:1.

Green leafy vegetable soup: If you prefer vegetables to fruits, then green leafy vegetable soup is a good alternative. Strain the soup well and give it diluted to the baby.

Cereals and dals: Thin gruels made from *dals* and rice can be given.

Vegetables: Cooked and mashed vegetables are recommended. Carrots, potatoes and leafy vegetables like spinach are ideal.

Fruits: Stew and mash fruits and then pass through a sieve. In fact one-year-olds prefer to have bananas without mashing.

Non-vegetarian foods: Egg yolk can be given either boiled or in the form of a soft custard. Egg white can cause allergies, so should be given after the tenth month.

childhood

Pre-school children (1 to 6 years)

The foundation for good eating habits is set in infancy. The changes made in the diet should be smooth and gradual. The aim is to give a balanced diet with sufficient calories. This is the period when children can suffer from lack of protein.

❶ Introduce only one new food at a time and then repeat if the child accepts it.

❷ Consider the child's likes and dislikes. Foods are appealing if the colour, size and presentation are attractive.

❸ Do not allow too many sugary and fried foods. Stick to regular meal times.

❹ Never force the child to eat.

❺ Never show a dislike for a particular food in the presence of the child, otherwise he/she will develop the dislike.

❻ Milk, eggs, carrots, yellow-orange fruits, green leafy vegetables, pulses should be included in the diet. Iron rich foods like *poha*, egg yolk and greens should be given.

School-going children (6-12 years)

❶ In school the child eats with other children and is easily influenced by their attitudes and tastes towards certain foods and new foods. Television advertising also has a great impact on the child's food likes and dislikes.

❷ Breakfast is the most important meal and eating breakfast has to be inculcated as a habit.

❸ The diet should contain foods from all five food groups but the demand for protein increases.

❹ Children of this age require more calcium to meet the demands of the developing bones.

❺ Foods rich in calories and protein are advisable so combine whole grains with pulses.

❻ Avoid junk foods like wafers, chips and noodles.

❼ Introduce fruits as a snack.

teenage or adolescence

Adolescence is the period of transition from childhood to adulthood. The final growth spurt takes place at this state. Girls mature faster, beginning around 8 years and ending at 13-15 years of age. For boys this period begins by 9 years and ends by 18 years. The skeletal growth means increased need for calcium. Well-balanced, nutritious diets prevent obesity and under-nutrition.

❶ Children of this age like to eat frequent snack type meals, so planning of snack food is very important. Choose high protein, high calorie snacks.

❷ Iron-rich foods like liver, nuts and oilseeds, jaggery, dates and leafy vegetables should be incorporated.

❸ Adolescents should be involved in a lot of outdoor games and activity so that their appetite is built up.

adulthood

This is the final growth phase of a normal lifecycle. The growth spurt stops. This is the phase when healthy eating can ensure a healthy old age. Balance, moderation and variety are necessary.

❶ Eat fruits and raw vegetables in the form of salads everyday for protection from obesity, diabetes, heart disease and digestive disorders.

❷ Eat protein 1gm/kg body weight so that muscular strength is maintained and the performance level is always high.

❸ Choose to have 40-60 % carbohydrates in the daily diet.

❹ Choose low-fat versions of foods – they help maintain the physique, keep the skin glowing and the heart healthy.

❺ Water is vital. Drink your daily quota sincerely.

pregnancy and lactation

Pregnancy

A woman who has been well-nourished before conception begins her pregnancy with reserves of several nutrients so that the needs of the growing foetus can be met without affecting her health. Energy and protein needs increase as both the mother and the foetus have to be provided for.

❶ Calcium requirement increases. Use of calcium and Vitamin A-rich foods reduces muscle cramps.

❷ Sources of Vitamin A are liver, egg yolk, butter, dark green leafy vegetables and yellow-orange vegetables and fruits.

❸ Dairy products, whole grains, leafy vegetables and nuts and oilseeds should be consumed.

❹ Iron-rich foods like liver, nuts, dried beans, eggs and leafy vegetables should be incorporated.

❺ Vitamin B and Folic acid needs also increase. Foods rich in them are whole grains, vegetables with skin, nuts and animal foods like fish, egg, liver, and other animal organs.

❻ Drink additional water during pregnancy.

❼ Keep a control on consumption of tea and coffee.

Lactation

The nutritional link between the mother and the child continues even after birth. The newborn solely depends on breast milk. Hormones control the process of lactation. A lactating mother's nutritional requirement should meet her own daily needs plus provide adequate nutrients for the growing infant. The mother should eat frequent meals to meet the energy requirements. Sometimes a mother has problems with attaining or maintaining adequate breast milk supply despite nursing frequently and on the baby's request and despite the baby latching well.Things used to increase milk supply are called galactagogues. Sucking is the best galactagogue and the mother's diet can include other galactagogue like milk, almonds, garden cress seeds and fenugreek seeds. Some also believe that fish and mutton increase secretion of milk.

menopause

Menopause is a natural process of aging in women. The average age of menopause is 42 to 56 years. A woman can say she has begun menopause when her menstrual cycle remains inactive for twelve months. Perimenopause refers to several years before menopause, when the symptoms just start. The symptoms are individualistic, but the few common ones are weight gain, night sweats, joint pain, fatigue, short-term memory loss, irregular bowel movement, insomnia, hot flushes in the day, itchy skin, mood swings and urinary tract infections. For optimum health and well-being during menopause, focus on a healthy nutritious diet.

❶ Boost intake of fruits like melons, bananas, oranges, lemons which are high in potassium. Potassium-rich foods help in sodium balance and prevent water retention. Also include dried fruits like apricots and figs.

❷ Eat lots of vegetables - in particular yam, dark green leafy vegetables, broccoli, cabbage, capsicum and tomato.

❸ Consume soy foods daily.

❹ Eat beans, sprouts and lentils regularly.

❺ Eat oily fish which is high in omega-3 fatty acids. Switch to olive oil.

❻ Cut down on processed foods and eat unprocessed foods like whole grain bread, oats and muesli. Instead of polished rice eat brown rice.

❼ Drink more water.

❽ Exercise regularly.

Male menopause (andropause) is the normal aging process in men. Men go through many emotional and physiological changes like women, after the age of forty. The symptoms are not as evident as in female menopause but do require attention. Common symptoms include weight gain, fatigue, hair loss and thinning of hair, lowered endurance and stamina, sleep disturbances, irritability, stiffness and impotency. For a sense of well-being during this phase, focus on a healthy nutritious diet, sleep for six to eight hours, engage in regular cardiovascular and strength training exercise and remember to have an annual physical fitness examination.

old age

Old age affects different people differently. Some feel useless and depressed as they grow older, and others feel they are evergreen! Aging is a natural process, so keeping a cheerful and positive approach enhances longevity. If one feels sad and run down, then the body becomes prone to more of the degenerative and infectious diseases. If one eats properly and in moderation, one will always feel good. Good health depends on good nutrition. An average human's adulthood can be extended by twenty percent if there is physical activity in their day-to-day life. If you are fit at 50, then the same can be continued till 70! Exercise is not only a preventive measure against heart diseases, it also increases the ability to withstand stress and the rate of metabolism. Exercise helps you maintain an ideal weight and reduces the risk of bone loss.

❶ Balance your diet.

❷ Plan your meals according to your likes and dislikes.

❸ Eat a variety of foods.

❹ Choose low-calorie, unrefined foods.

❺ Incorporate good quality protein from beans, fish, chicken, dals and sprouts in your diet.

❻ Consume low-fat dairy products and soya.

❼ Select foods with low sugar and low fat content.

❽ Pay attention to the increased equirement of calcium, iron and zinc. Include high fibre foods like fruits, green leafy vegetables, whole grains and natural cereals.

tofu rassedaar

Ingredients

250 grams bean curd (tofu), cut into 1-inch cubes
1 tablespoon olive oil
1 teaspoon cumin seeds
2 inches ginger, chopped
2 medium tomatoes, puréed
Salt to taste
½ teaspoon red chilli powder
1 teaspoon coriander power
A pinch of turmeric powder
½ cup skimmed milk yogurt, whisked
1 green chilli, chopped
A pinch of *garam masala* powder
2 tablespoons chopped fresh coriander

Method

❶ Heat the oil in a pan and add the cumin seeds. When they begin
to change colour, add the ginger, tomato purée and salt and sauté for
two minutes.

❷ Add the chilli, coriander and turmeric powders and cook for one
minute. Stir in the yogurt and green chilli and cook for two minutes.

❸ Add the tofu, *garam masala* powder and fresh coriander and serve.

It takes some time to get to like tofu but remembering its nutritive
value helps. It is rich in protein, calcium and iron and tastes almost
like cottage cheese. Tofu and yogurt are amiable partners. This mildly
spiced curry is super-quick to make and goes well with hot *roti*. If you
want, you can decrease the amount of yogurt and make it a side-dish
of dry but well-coated tofu.

khumb hara dhania

Ingredients

600 grams fresh button mushrooms, trimmed
1 cup chopped fresh coriander
1 tablespoon olive oil
5 green cardamoms
1 black cardamom
5 cloves
1 inch cinnamon
1 bay leaf
A pinch of mace powder
¾ cup Boiled Onion Paste (Vol. 5, page 68)
4 teaspoons minced ginger
4 teaspoons minced garlic
4 green chillies, chopped
1 teaspoon red chilli powder
½ teaspoon coriander powder
1½ cups skimmed milk yogurt, whisked
Salt to taste
1 tablespoon cashew nut paste
2 tablespoons melon seed paste
1½ inches ginger, cut into thin strips

Method

❶ Blanch the mushrooms in hot water for two minutes. Drain and set aside.

❷ Heat the oil in a non-stick *kadai*. Add the green cardamoms, black cardamom, cloves, cinnamon, bay leaf and mace powder and sauté over medium heat until fragrant.

❸ Add the boiled onion paste and sauté for two to three minutes. Stir in the minced ginger and garlic and continue to sauté until the oil rises to the surface. Add the green chillies and sauté for thirty seconds more, before adding the chilli and coriander powders. Stir for another thirty seconds.

❹ Remove from the heat and stir in the yogurt and salt. Mix well. Return the *kadai* to the heat. Add three-fourth cup of water and bring to a boil. Lower the heat and simmer until the oil rises to the surface.

❺ Stir in the cashew nut paste and melon seed paste and simmer for two to three minutes.

❻ Add the mushrooms and three-fourth cup of fresh coriander and simmer for two to three minutes.

❼ Transfer the mushrooms to a serving dish and garnish with the remaining fresh coriander and the ginger strips and serve hot.

Mushrooms have a wonderful ability to absorb flavours. This recipe uses mild spices but lots of fresh coriander to coat the mushrooms with a succulent *masala*. Serve simply with steamed brown rice or with wholewheat *rotis*.

palak bahaar

Ingredients

2 bunches (700 grams) spinach
3 green chillies
1½ tablespoons rice bran oil
1 inch ginger, chopped
4 garlic cloves, chopped
1 large onion, chopped
¼ teaspoon nutmeg powder
2 medium carrots,
cut into thin diagonal slices
5-6 French beans, cut into diamond-
shaped pieces
¼ medium cauliflower,
 separated into small florets
½ teaspoon cumin seeds
2 medium tomatoes, chopped
1 teaspoon lemon juice
Salt to taste
1½ teaspoons red chilli powder
2 teaspoons *garam masala* powder
2 tablespoons chopped fresh coriander

Method

❶ Blanch the spinach in boiling hot water for two to three minutes. Drain excess water and refresh in cold water. Purée in a blender along with one green chilli. Chop the remaining green chillies.

❷ Heat half the oil in a non-stick pan, add the ginger and garlic and stir-fry.

❸ Add the onion and green chillies and sauté till the onion is lightly browned. Add the nutmeg powder and continue cooking on medium heat for a couple of minutes, stirring frequently.

❹ Add the puréed spinach, cook for a minute and add salt. Set aside.

❺ Blanch the carrots, French beans and cauliflower.

❻ Heat the remaining oil in another non-stick pan, add the cumin seeds and when it starts to change colour, add the tomatoes. Cook on a medium heat for three to four minutes, stirring continuously. Add the blanched vegetables and stir-fry lightly.

❼ Add the lemon juice and season with salt and chilli powder. Lastly add the *garam masala* powder and fresh coriander.

❽ Spread the prepared spinach on a flat serving dish, place the cooked vegetables in the centre and serve hot.

Palak Bahaar is a festive presentation and has a sweet warmth to it thanks to the nutmeg powder. Nutmeg is good for the heart.

methi baingan

Ingredients

2 bunches (700 grams) fresh fenugreek, chopped
10-12 small brinjals
Salt to taste
2 teaspoons red chilli powder
½ teaspoon dried mango powder
1 tablespoon olive oil/rice bran oil
½ teaspoon mustard seeds
8-10 curry leaves
1 green chilli, chopped
2 medium onions, chopped
1½ tablespoons ginger-garlic paste
2 medium tomatoes, chopped
1 teaspoon cumin powder
1 teaspoon coriander powder
½ teaspoon turmeric powder
½ teaspoon *garam masala* powder
2 tablespoons chopped fresh coriander

Method

❶ Slit the brinjals lengthways into four keeping the stem intact.

❷ Rub the salt, one teaspoon of chilli powder and the dried mango powder into the slit brinjals and set aside.

❸ Heat the oil in a pressure cooker; add the mustard seeds. When they begin to splutter, add the curry leaves, green chilli and onions and sauté on medium heat till the onions turn golden.

❹ Add the ginger-garlic paste and continue to sauté for one minute. Stir in the chopped tomatoes and remaining chilli powder, cumin and coriander powders. Add the turmeric powder, *garam masala* powder and half a cup of water and bring the mixture to a boil.

❺ Add the brinjals, fresh fenugreek and salt. Seal the cooker with the lid and cook till the pressure is released once (one whistle). Lower the heat and cook for two minutes.

❻ Take the cooker off the heat and remove the lid when the pressure has reduced.

❼ Garnish with the fresh coriander and serve hot.

Fenugreek is rich in calcium, beta-carotene, iron, Vitamin C and also antioxidants. It is very good for those suffering from iron deficiency and for pregnant as well as lactating women. Brinjal is high in fibre and improves bowel movement. Definitely a great combination.

palak paneer

Ingredients

1 large bunch (900 grams) fresh spinach
200 grams skimmed milk cottage cheese,
cut into ½-inch cubes
2-3 green chillies, chopped
1½ tablespoons olive oil
½ teaspoon cumin seeds
8-10 garlic cloves, chopped
Salt to taste
1 tablespoon lemon juice
2 tablespoons cream

Method

❶ Remove the stems and wash the spinach thoroughly in running water. Blanch in salted boiling water for two minutes. Refresh in chilled water. Squeeze out the excess water. Grind the spinach into a fine paste along with the green chillies.

❷ Heat the oil in a pan. Add the cumin seeds. When they begin to change colour, add the garlic and sauté for half a minute. Add the spinach purée and stir. Check the seasoning. Add water if required.

❸ When the gravy comes to a boil, add the cottage cheese cubes and mix well. Stir in the lemon juice. Finally add the cream.

❹ Serve hot.

Favourite Punjabi special! This dish is low in spices but high in taste and nutrition, since spinach is a leafy green vegetable containing iron and calcium. But take care not to overcook it as it will not only adversely affect the bright green colour but also the taste.

quick pressure-cooked vegetables

Ingredients

1 medium potato, cut into ½-inch pieces
2 medium carrots, cut into ½-inch pieces
½ small cauliflower, separated into small florets
¼ small cabbage, cut into ½-inch pieces
10-12 French beans, cut into ½-inch pieces
½ small bottle gourd, cut into ½-inch pieces
1 medium tomato, cut into 8 pieces
1 medium green capsicum,
cut into ½-inch pieces
1 teaspoon olive oil
1 bay leaf
8-10 black peppercorns, crushed
½ teaspoon roasted cumin powder
Salt to taste

Method

❶ Soak the potato pieces in water.

❷ Heat the oil in a pressure cooker, add the bay leaf and peppercorns and stir-fry briefly. Add all the vegetables, roasted cumin powder and salt and mix well. Stir-fry for two to three minutes.

❸ Cover and cook under pressure for five to six minutes. Remove from heat.

❹ Serve immediately.

Pressure-cooking not only saves time and fuel, but also retains the nutrients, colour and flavour if cooked for the right time. Pressure-cooking is one of the healthier alternatives for people who like to cook with minimum oil.

shahi paneer

Ingredients

400 grams skimmed milk cottage
cheese
2 large onions, quartered
1 tablespoon rice bran oil
3 cloves
4-5 black peppercorns
2 one-inch sticks cinnamon
1 bay leaf
2 green chillies, slit
1 teaspoon ginger paste
1 teaspoon garlic paste
1 tablespoon cashew nut paste
2 tablespoons melon seed paste
½ cup skimmed milk yogurt
½ cup low-fat cream
A pinch of saffron
½ teaspoon *garam masala* powder
Salt to taste
¼ teaspoon green cardamom powder

Method

❶ Cut the cottage cheese into half-inch wide and one-inch long pieces.

❷ Boil the onions in quarter cup of water. Drain and allow it to cool. Grind to a fine paste.

❸ Heat the oil in a non-stick *kadai*, add the cloves, black peppercorns, cinnamon and bay leaf and sauté till fragrant.

❹ Add the green chillies and boiled onion paste and sauté for three to four minutes on low heat so that it retains its colour.

❺ Add the ginger paste and garlic paste and continue to sauté for half a minute.

❻ Add the cashew nut paste and melon seed paste and sauté for a further two minutes.

❼ Add the yogurt and sauté till the water from the yogurt is absorbed.

❽ Add the cream, saffron and *garam masala* powder and stir. Add salt to taste.

❾ Add the cottage cheese and stir gently.

❿ Sprinkle the cardamom powder and serve hot.

This is a favourite amongst cottage cheese lovers! The oil is minimal as the nuts and seeds add good-quality fats to the recipe. If you have any left over, refrigerate it as it tastes great the following day too!

urulai chettinad

Ingredients

500 grams baby potatoes, halved
4 dried red chillies
2 tablespoons skinless split black gram
10-12 black peppercorns
2½ tablespoons extra virgin olive oil
1 teaspoon mustard seeds
20 curry leaves
20 shallots
Salt to taste

Method

❶ Dry-roast the dried chillies, split black gram and black peppercorns. Cool and pound to a coarse powder.

❷ Heat the extra virgin olive oil in a non-stick *kadai*. Add the mustard seeds, curry leaves and shallots and sauté till lightly browned.

❸ Add the potatoes, stir and add salt. Cover and cook on medium heat for eight to ten minutes or till the potatoes are almost done.

❹ Add the *masala* powder and mix. Cover and cook over low heat for about three to four minutes or till the potatoes are done.

❺ Serve hot.

Local vegetables like brinjals, potato, unripe banana etc. dominate the traditional vegetarian preparations in Tamil Nadu's Chettinad cuisine. No recipe is complete without the use of curry leaves.

wadian aloo

Ingredients

2-3 large dried *urad dal* nuggets (*wadian*)
4 medium potatoes
2½ tablespoons rice bran oil
1 teaspoon cumin seeds
1 large onion, chopped
1 inch ginger, chopped
A pinch of asafoetida
½ teaspoon turmeric powder
2 teaspoons coriander powder
½ teaspoon cumin powder
1½ teaspoons red chilli powder
Salt to taste
2 large tomatoes, chopped
½ teaspoon *garam masala* powder
2 tablespoons chopped fresh coriander

Method

❶ Break the *wadian* into small pieces.

❷ Wash the potatoes and cut, without peeling, into eight pieces each.

❸ Heat one-and-a-half tablespoons of oil in a non-stick pan; add the broken *wadian* and roast till fragrant. Drain on absorbent paper and then soak in one cup of water.

❹ Heat the remaining oil in another non-stick pan; add the cumin seeds and onion and sauté for three minutes.

❺ Add the ginger, asafoetida, turmeric powder, coriander powder, cumin powder, chilli powder salt and potatoes.

❻ Stir well and add three cups of water and the *wadian*. Cover and cook till the potatoes are done.

❼ Add the tomatoes and cook for five minutes.

❽ Sprinkle the *garam masala* powder and fresh coriander and serve hot.

Note: Wadian from Amritsar are very tasty, but very spicy.

This dish transports me to my childhood in Ambala. When my mother cooks it, believe it or not, I lick the dish clean. *Urad dal* is an excellent source of protein and Vitamin B, which are extremely important for growing children, pregnant and lactating women. All the spices like asafoetida, ginger and cumin powder aid digestion and reduce flatulence.

undhiyo

Ingredients

25-30 broad beans, cut into
1-inch pieces
6-8 small potatoes, diced
100 grams purple yam, diced
2 unripe bananas, diced
3-4 small brinjals
2 inch ginger
6-8 garlic cloves
4 green chillies
3 tablespoons chopped fresh coriander
2 tablespoons rice bran oil
A pinch of asafoetida
1 teaspoon mustard seeds
Salt to taste
1 teaspoon turmeric powder
¼ cup grated coconut

Muthiya
¼ cup gram flour
½ cup chopped fresh fenugreek
½ inch ginger, grated
1-2 green chillies, chopped
Salt to taste

Method

❶ Grind the ginger, garlic and green chillies to a paste. Add the fresh coriander and mix.

❷ To make the *muthiyas*, mix all the *muthiya* ingredients to make a stiff dough. Divide into small portions and shape each into one-inch long and half-inch thick rolls. Heat sufficient water in a steamer. Place the *muthiyas* on the perforated plate and place the plate in the steamer. Steam for fifteen to twenty minutes. Remove and set aside.

❸ Heat the oil in a non-stick deep pan; add the asafoetida and mustard seeds. When the mustard seeds begin to splutter, add the ginger-garlic-green chilli paste and broad beans. Place the rest of the vegetables in layers one on top of the other. Sprinkle the salt and turmeric powder. Cook for five minutes on high heat.

❹ Pour one cup of water, cover and simmer on very low heat for twenty to twenty five minutes.

❺ Add the steamed *muthiyas* and continue to cook for five minutes. Toss the vegetables occasionally but do not stir.

❻ Serve hot, garnished with the coconut.

A seasonal winter dish, turning out the perfect *undhiyo* takes some practice. There are no expensive ingredients yet it tastes exotic. Ensure that you buy fresh vegetables. One of the most popular Gujarati dishes, *undhiyo* can be high in calories if prepared in the traditional way. We have made subtle changes like steaming the *muthiyas* instead of deep-frying them.

bean curd with french beans and hoisin sauce

Ingredients

200 grams firm bean curd (tofu)
250 grams French beans, halved
3 tablespoons hoisin sauce
1 tablespoon sesame oil
1 inch ginger, sliced
10 garlic cloves, chopped
1 medium onion, sliced
1 tablespoon red chilli sauce
1 tablespoon soy sauce
Salt to taste

Method

❶ Cut the bean curd into half-inch thick fingers.

❷ Heat the sesame oil in a pan. Add the ginger and garlic and sauté for two minutes. Add the onion and sauté for further two minutes.

❸ Add the hoisin sauce to the onion along with red chilli sauce and mix. Add the French beans and mix.

❹ Add the bean curd, soy sauce and salt. Toss gently.

❺ Serve hot.

Stir-fries are great: they look pretty, taste excellent and require minimal effort. I prefer serving this with steamed rice. For dieters this is an excellent choice as it is high in protein and low in fat.

five-spice stir-fry

Ingredients

200 grams noodles, boiled
1 tablespoon cornflour
1 cup orange juice
2 tablespoons olive oil
5-6 garlic cloves, chopped
8-10 French beans, diagonally sliced
1 medium carrot, sliced
8-10 broccoli florets
1 medium onion, sliced
Salt to taste
1 tablespoon soy sauce
2 teaspoons crushed red chillies
1 teaspoon five-spice powder
7-8 fresh button mushrooms, quartered
½ tablespoon honey
¼ teaspoon MSG (optional)

Method

❶ Mix the cornflour in orange juice.

❷ Heat one tablespoon oil in a non-stick wok. Add the garlic and sauté for half a minute. Add the French beans, carrots and broccoli and stir-fry for two to three minutes.

❸ Add the onion, salt, soy sauce, half the crushed red chillies, five-spice powder and continue to stir-fry for three to four minutes.

❹ Add the mushrooms, honey and MSG.

❺ Add the cornflour mixed in orange juice. Stir and cook till thickened.

❻ Heat the remaining oil in another non-stick pan. Add the boiled noodles and stir-fry for two minutes.

❼ Transfer the noodles onto a plate. Pour the sauce over. Sprinkle the remaining crushed red chillies on top and serve hot.

The five-spice sauce delicately glazes the vegetables... perfect partner for the noodles. Broccoli adds colour and texture and also fibre and antioxidants.

tortilla with grilled vegetables and rice

Ingredients

4 tortillas
Chilli sauce as required

Grilled vegetables
1 medium green capsicum,
cut into small triangles
2 medium onions,
quartered and layers separated
2 small carrots, cut into small triangles
¼ small broccoli, separated
into small florets
1 tablespoon olive oil
Salt to taste
½ teaspoon crushed red chillies

Rice
1 tablespoon olive oil
1 medium onion, chopped
2-3 garlic cloves, chopped
1 cup rice, boiled
4 tablespoons Salsa (Vol. 5, page 67)
Salt to taste
2 tablespoons chopped fresh coriander
1 teaspoon dried herbs

Method

❶ For the grilled vegetables, heat the oil in a non-stick pan. Add the capsicum, onions and carrots and sauté without stirring so that they burn slightly. Stir. Add the broccoli and cook for some time. Add the salt and crushed red chillies and mix.

❷ For the rice, heat the oil in another non-stick pan. Add the onion and garlic and stir. Cook for three to four minutes. Add the boiled rice and salsa. Mix and add the coriander leaves and dried herbs. Mix and set aside.

❸ Add one tablespoon of chilli sauce to the vegetables and stir.

❹ Place the tortillas on a flat surface. Place some rice on it and top it up with the grilled vegetables. Drizzle chilli sauce on top and roll.

❺ Wrap in butter paper and serve.

It sometimes becomes essential to tempt children with healthy foods such as this! I make this often as a TV dinner and as grilling needs very little oil, I am happy that the fat content is reduced.

vegetable stew with garlic bread

Ingredients

2 medium carrots, cut into 1-inch pieces
¼ small cauliflower, separated into florets
¼ cup green peas
2 medium potatoes, cut into 1-inch pieces
1 medium zucchini, cut into 1-inch pieces
1 inch ginger, sliced
3-4 cloves
8-10 black peppercorns
1 teaspoon cumin seeds
1 medium onion, sliced
4⅓ cups Vegetable Stock (Vol. 5, page 66)
Salt to taste
1 celery stalk, cut into 1-inch pieces
3-4 black peppercorns, crushed
5 fresh spinach leaves, shredded
1 loaf of garlic bread, sliced

Method

❶ Blanch the carrots, cauliflower and green peas individually in boiling water. Refresh and set aside.

❷ Tie the ginger, cloves, peppercorns and cumin seeds in a piece of muslin to make a *bouquet garni.*

❸ Heat a non-stick pan. Add the onion and roast it lightly. Add the vegetable stock and bring it to a boil.

❹ Add the *bouquet garni* to the boiling stock. Season with salt.

❺ Add the potatoes. Cover and cook over medium heat. Once the potatoes are cooked, remove the *bouquet garni* and mash the potatoes so that it thickens the stock.

❻ Add the celery, zucchini, carrots, cauliflower, peas and cook on low heat for two minutes. Adjust the salt and add the peppercorns.

❼ Add the spinach and mix.

❽ Lightly toast the slices of garlic bread and serve with the hot stew.

Vegetable Stew with Garlic Bread is the ideal combination for a small family dinner and large parties! It also has a number of nutrients.

chinese garlic mushrooms

Ingredients

20-24 medium fresh button mushrooms
16-20 garlic cloves
1 tablespoon lemon juice
1 teaspoon light soy sauce
½ teaspoon white pepper powder
¼ teaspoon MSG (optional)
Salt to taste
3 tablespoons rice bran oil
2 tablespoons cornflour
2-3 dried red chillies, broken in half
4 tablespoons tomato sauce
1 tablespoon white vinegar
2 tablespoons red chilli paste
1 tablespoon hot black bean paste
1 teaspoon sugar
1 cup Vegetable Stock (Vol. 5, page 66)
½ medium green capsicum, cut into ½-inch diamonds
½ medium red capsicum, cut into ½-inch diamonds
1 medium onion, quartered and layers separated
1 spring onion, finely sliced
1 teaspoon sesame oil
1 tablespoon red chilli flakes

Method

❶ Grind six cloves of garlic to a smooth paste and chop the rest.

❷ Mix the garlic paste, lemon juice, soy sauce, white pepper powder, MSG and salt to taste. Marinate the mushrooms in this mixture for ten to fifteen minutes.

❸ Heat one-and-a-half tablespoons oil in a non-stick wok and sauté the marinated mushrooms on moderate heat, turning frequently until golden brown. Drain and set aside.

❹ Mix two tablespoons of cornflour and one cup of water.

❺ Heat the remaining oil in the same wok; add the red chillies and chopped garlic and stir-fry for a few seconds. Add the tomato sauce, vinegar, red chilli paste, hot black bean paste, sugar and salt to taste. Stir in the vegetable stock and continue to cook on high heat for one minute.

❻ Add the capsicums, onion and spring onion and cook for a couple of minutes more. Stir in the cornflour mixture and cook, stirring continuously, till the sauce starts to thicken.

❼ Stir the sautéed mushrooms into the sauce and toss well to coat. Drizzle the sesame oil, sprinkle the chilli flakes and serve hot.

Mushrooms add a lot of texture and flavour to every dish. Garlic, by itself, is heart-friendly.

stir-fried tofu with asian greens

Ingredients

200 grams bean curd (tofu),
cut into ¾-inch cubes
2 tablespoons oil
Salt to taste
2 inches ginger, grated
½ teaspoon black pepper powder
1 tablespoon lemon juice
½ medium broccoli, florets, blanched
4 Chinese cabbages (pak choy), roughly cut
4-5 cabbage leaves, shredded
10 garlic cloves, chopped
1 tablespoon soy sauce

Method

❶ Heat one tablespoon oil in a non-stick pan, add the tofu cubes and stir-fry for three to four minutes on medium heat. Sprinkle salt, grated ginger, black pepper powder and lemon juice.

❷ Heat the remaining oil in another non-stick pan. Add the broccoli florets, pak choy and cabbage and sauté for two minutes. Sprinkle a little water. Add the garlic, soy sauce and a little more water. Cook till the vegetables soften slightly.

❸ Transfer the greens onto a serving plate. Place the tofu pieces on them and serve hot.

A pleasant base of greens with subtly-flavoured tofu... this dish is a palate cleanser! Stir-fries have many advantages. They need less oil for cooking and retain the nutrients in the vegetables used. Here broccoli and cabbage add fibre, Vitamin C and antioxidants. Ginger adds bite and aids in digestion.

grilled salt and pepper tofu

Ingredients

200 grams bean curd (tofu),
cut into ½-inch cubes
Sea salt to taste
2 spring onions, chopped
1 inch ginger, chopped
2-inch celery stalk, chopped
2 green chillies, chopped
3-4 garlic cloves, chopped
½ teaspoon black pepper powder
2 stalks spring onion greens, chopped

Method

❶ Sprinkle salt over the tofu and mix lightly.

❷ Heat a non-stick pan till very hot. Place the tofu over it so that it browns immediately. Turn and cook the other side as well.

❸ Transfer the tofu to a bowl. Add the spring onions, ginger, celery, green chillies and garlic to the same pan and mix on high heat. Add the browned tofu along with a little salt and black pepper powder and toss again. Remove.

❹ Sprinkle the spring onion greens, mix and serve immediately.

This dish is one of the quickest to make and one of the lightest to eat. It is very low in carbohydrates and calories, so perfect for a light snack. Or you could roll the tofu in a *roti* with some salad and chutney for a delicious portable lunch.

sichuan vegetables

Ingredients

½ medium head broccoli, separated
into small florets
8-10 snow peas, halved
4-6 fresh button mushrooms, sliced
1 medium red capsicum, seeded and
cut into 1-inch pieces
1 medium yellow capsicum, seeded and
cut into 1-inch pieces
1 medium green capsicum, seeded
and cut into 1-inch pieces
1½ tablespoons olive oil
4-5 garlic cloves, crushed
2 spring onions, chopped
1 celery stalk, chopped
1½ tablespoons red chilli paste
8-10 Sichuan peppers (optional)
1 teaspoon sugar
Salt to taste
¼ teaspoon MSG (optional)
2 cups Vegetable Stock (Vol.5, page 66)
3 tablespoons cornflour
1 tablespoon white vinegar

Method

❶ Heat the oil in a non-stick wok or pan; add the garlic,
spring onions and celery and stir-fry for one minute.
Add the red chilli paste, Sichuan peppers, sugar, salt
and MSG. Add half a cup of vegetable stock and cook
for one minute.

❷ Add the broccoli florets, snow peas, mushrooms
and capsicums and stir-fry for two minutes. Stir in
the remaining vegetable stock and cook on high heat
for a couple of minutes.

❸ Mix the cornflour in one cup of water and stir
into the pan. Cook on medium heat for one minute
until the sauce starts to thicken, stirring occasionally.

❹ Stir in the vinegar and mix well. Serve hot.

Traditional Sichuan food is known to be hot-spicy-
sweet-sour focusing more on meat, poultry and fish.
This vegetable preparation has the same base though
I have brought down the 'heat' meter!

soya granule lasagne

Ingredients

1 cup soya granules, soaked
8 ready-made lasagne sheets
Salt to taste
2 tablespoons olive oil
3 tablespoons skimmed milk
3-4 garlic cloves, chopped
1 medium onion, chopped
3 medium tomatoes, chopped
½ cup tomato ketchup
1 cup White Sauce (Vol. 5, page 68)
4-5 fresh basil leaves
2 teaspoons crushed red chillies
½ cup grated cheese
¼ teaspoon mixed herbs

Method

❶ Boil seven to eight cups of water in a large wide mouthed pan. Add a little salt. Slide in the lasagne sheets and cook till *al dente*. Drain and refresh in cold water.

❷ Heat one tablespoon oil in another pan. Add the soaked soya granules. Add the milk and let it cook. Add the salt, mix and set aside.

❸ Heat the remaining oil in another pan. Add the garlic and sauté for a minute. Add the onion and sauté till translucent. Add the tomatoes and cook till they turn pulpy. Add the tomato ketchup and cook for one more minute. Add the white sauce and let it come to a boil. Adjust the salt. Remove from heat and add the basil leaves and half the crushed red chillies and mix well.

❹ Preheat an oven to 180°C/350°F/Gas Mark 4.

❺ Spread some of the prepared sauce in a baking dish. Place a few lasagne sheets so that the base is fully covered. Spread half the soya mixture over it. Place some more lasagne sheets over to cover the filling fully.

❻ Repeat the above layers once taking care to end with the sauce layer. Spread the grated cheese evenly over the sauce.

❼ Sprinkle the remaining crushed red chillies and mixed herbs. Place in the preheated oven and bake for at least twenty five minutes or till the cheese layer is golden brown.

❽ Serve hot.

Lasagne and soya smothered in a cheesy herb sauce is a marvellous dish for all those who don't like their food too spicy. Soya granules are a good source of protein. A wonderful dish for fussy teenagers – they will simply lap it up what with the inviting layer of cheese!

stir-fried bean curd with lemon grass and chillies

Ingredients

675 grams firm bean curd (tofu),
cut into 1-inch cubes
2 one-inch lemon grass stalks,
bruised and chopped
2 fresh red chillies, seeded
and chopped
3 tablespoons oil
1 cup Vegetable Stock (Vol. 5, page 66)
4 tablespoons hoisin sauce
2 tablespoons soy sauce
1½ tablespoons tomato purée
2 leeks (only the white part), sliced
1 large red capsicum, seeded and
cut into 1-inch squares
1 large green capsicum, seeded and
cut into 1-inch squares
12 button mushrooms, halved
½ teaspoon black pepper powder

Method

❶ Place the bean curd cubes between double layers of paper towels and press gently so that all the extra moisture is absorbed.

❷ Heat two tablespoons oil in a non-stick pan and sauté the bean curd cubes, a few at a time, on medium heat till golden all around. Drain on absorbent paper.

❸ Mix together the vegetable stock, hoisin sauce, soy sauce, tomato purée and fresh red chillies in a bowl.

❹ Heat the remaining oil in another non-stick wok. Add the leeks and lemon grass and stir-fry over medium heat for about one minute or till tender. Add the capsicums and mushrooms and stir-fry for a further one minute.

❺ Stir in the sauce mixture and fried bean curd and bring the mixture to a boil. Cook on medium heat, stirring frequently, for about two minutes or till the sauce thickens slightly.

❻ Transfer into a serving dish, sprinkle black pepper powder and serve immediately.

Spicy, soft and really delicious... be careful not to break the bean curd into smaller pieces. Bean curd might be delicate to handle but is a known power food due to its protein richness. It is an excellent substitute for *paneer* in most dishes. The lactose-intolerant can enjoy the bean curd.

til moongphali aloo

Ingredients

750 grams baby potatoes
1 tablespoon sesame seeds
2 tablespoons roasted peanuts,
coarsely crushed
Salt to taste
1 tablespoon olive oil
1 teaspoon cumin seeds
4 green chillies, chopped
1 inch ginger, chopped
1 tablespoon garlic paste
1 teaspoon roasted cumin powder
1 teaspoon red chilli powder
1½ tablespoons grated fresh coconut
1 teaspoon *garam masala* powder
2 teaspoons lemon juice
2 tablespoons chopped fresh coriander

Method

❶ Parboil the unpeeled potatoes in salted water and set aside. Press them lightly.

❷ Heat the oil in a non-stick *kadai*; add the cumin seeds, green chillies and ginger. When the seeds begin to change colour, add the garlic paste and sauté for two or three minutes. Add the potatoes and toss well.

❸ Add the sesame seeds, peanuts, roasted cumin powder, chilli powder, coconut and *garam masala* powder. Adjust salt.

❹ Continue to cook for five minutes, tossing continuously. Stir in the lemon juice.

❺ Serve hot, garnished with the fresh coriander.

Potato skins are a good source of insoluble fibre along with being a storehouse of nutrients. Cooking potatoes in their skins protects the nutrients that otherwise escape from peeled potatoes during the cooking process. *Til* and *moongphali* increase the protein content in the dish.

punjabi bhindi

Ingredients

500 grams ladies' fingers
1 tablespoon rice bran oil
½ teaspoon cumin seeds
3 large onions, thickly sliced
1 green chilli, slit
½ teaspoon red chilli powder
1 teaspoon coriander powder
¼ teaspoon turmeric powder
Salt to taste
½ teaspoon dried mango powder

Method

❶ Trim the heads and tails of the ladies' fingers and cut into two-inch long pieces. Slit each horizontally without cutting through.

❷ Heat the oil in a non-stick *kadai* and add the cumin seeds. Sauté briefly, then add the onions and green chilli and sauté for thirty seconds.

❸ Add the ladies' fingers and chilli, coriander and turmeric powders. Mix well, cover and cook over low heat for five to seven minutes, stirring occasionally. Add the salt and dried mango powder and cook for a further two minutes.

❹ Serve hot.

Visit a Punjabi home in the summer and you will not need to guess what's cooking! Okra or ladies' fingers *(bhindi)* cooked in this simple manner, are delicious with any curry and *roti*. Bhindi is rich in folic acid, Vitamins C, K and B and also in phosphorus and potassium.

steamed lauki and palak kofta

Ingredients

For the koftas

1 small (250 grams) bottle gourd, peeled and grated
2 medium bunches (350 grams each) fresh spinach
Salt to taste
3 medium potatoes, boiled and mashed
2-3 green chillies, chopped
1 tablespoon raisins
3 tablespoons coarse rice powder
½ teaspoon chaat masala
1 teaspoon ginger paste
1 teaspoon garlic paste
1 large onion, chopped

For the curry

1 teaspoon ginger paste
1 teaspoon garlic paste
1 large onion, chopped
1 teaspoon red chilli powder
¼ teaspoon turmeric powder
½ teaspoon garam masala powder
1 teaspoon dried fenugreek leaves, roasted and crushed
5-6 medium tomatoes, puréed
1½ tablespoons honey
Salt to taste
2 tablespoons chopped fresh coriander

Method

❶ For the kofta, add the salt to grated bottle gourd and set aside for five minutes. Squeeze out excess water. Blanch the spinach in sufficient boiling water for one minute. Drain. Refresh in cold water. Squeeze out excess water and chop.

❷ Mix the blanched bottle gourd and spinach with the potatoes, green chillies, raisins, rice powder, chaat masala, ginger paste, garlic paste, onion and salt in a large bowl.

❸ Divide into twenty equal portions and shape into oval koftas. Steam them in a steamer for fifteen-twenty minutes. Set aside.

❹ For the curry heat a non-stick pan. Roast the ginger paste, garlic paste and onion on medium heat for five to six minutes. Add the chilli, turmeric and garam masala powders, dried fenugreek leaves and two tablespoons of water and cook for a minute.

❺ Add the tomato purée, honey and salt. Add one cup of water and simmer for ten minutes.

❻ Arrange the steamed koftas in a serving plate, pour the gravy over and serve immediately garnished with the fresh coriander.

Koftas made traditionally would require them to be deep-fried. The healthier option is to steam them. I have used two fibrous vegetables like bottle gourd and spinach so that the final koftas are soft and absorbent in the gravy. Steaming requires no added fat.